NURSERY RHYMES

ILLUSTRATIONS BY
MARGARET TARRANT

THE O'BRIEN PRESS
DUBLIN

CONTENTS

Little Bo-Peep

Little Bo-Peep, she lost her sheep,
    And didn't know where to find them;
Leave them alone and they'll come home,
    And carry their tails behind them.

Little Bo-Peep fell fast asleep,
    And dreamt she heard them bleating;
When she awoke, 'twas all a joke,
    For they were still a-fleeting.

Then she took her little crook,
    Determined for to find them;
She found them indeed, but it made her
       heart bleed,
    For they'd left their tails behind them.

It happened one day, as Bo-Peep did stray,
    Into a meadow hard by,
There she espied their tails side by side,
    All hung on a tree to dry.

She heaved a sigh and wiped her eye,
    Then went o'er hill and dale,
And tried what she could, as a shepherdess
       should,
    To tack each sheep to its tail.

Margaret W Tarrant.

See-Saw
Margery Daw

See-saw, Margery Daw,
    Johnnie shall have a new master;
He shall have but a penny a day
    Because he can't work any faster.

Jack and Jill

Jack and Jill
   went up the hill
To fetch a pail
   of water;
Jack fell down and
   broke his crown
And Jill came
   tumbling after.

To Market, To Market

To market, to market,
    To buy a fat pig;
Home again, home again
    Jiggety jig.
To market, to market,
    To buy a fat hog;
Home again, home again,
    Jiggety jog.

This little pig went to market,

This little pig stayed at home;

This little pig had roast beef,

This little pig had none;

This little pig cried "Wee wee, wee, wee!" All the way home.

Sing a Song of Sixpence

Sing a song of sixpence,
    A pocket full of rye;
Four and twenty blackbirds,
    Baked in a pie.

When the pie was opened,
    The birds began to sing,
Wasn't that a dainty dish
    To set before the king?

The king was in the counting-house,
    Counting out his money;
The queen was in her parlour
    Eating bread and honey.

The maid was in the garden,
    Hanging out some clothes,
When down came a blackbird,
    And pecked off her nose.

NOTE: But down came little Jenny Wren
And popped it on again

Pussy Cat, Pussy Cat

"Pussycat, pussycat, where have you been?"
"I've been to London, to visit the Queen."

"Pussycat, pussycat, what did you there?"
"I frightened a little mouse under her chair."

The Queen of Hearts

The Queen of Hearts
She made some tarts,
All on a summer's day;

The Knave of Hearts,
He stole the tarts,
And took them clean away.

The King of Hearts
Called for the tarts,
And beat the Knave full sore;

The Knave of Hearts
Brought back the tarts,
And vowed he'd steal no more.

Little Jack Horner

Little Jack Horner
    Sat in a corner,
Eating his Christmas pie;
    He put in his thumb
And pulled out a plum,

Saying, "Oh what a good boy am I!"

Little Miss Muffet,
Sat on a tuffet,
Eating her curds
and whey:

There came a great spider,
And sat down
beside her,

And frightened
Miss Muffet
away!

Margaret W. Tarrant

Hickery Dickery Dock!

Hickery, Dickery, Dock!
The mouse ran up the clock,
The clock struck one,
The mouse ran down,
Hickery, Dickery, Dock.

What Can the Matter Be?

Oh dear, what can the matter be?
Oh dear, what can the matter be?
Oh dear, what can the matter be?
    Johnnie's so long at the fair.

He promised to buy me a bunch of blue ribbons,
He promised to buy me a bunch of blue ribbons,
He promised to buy me a bunch of blue ribbons,
    To tie up my bonnie brown hair.

He promised to bring me a basket of posies,
A garland of lilies, a garland of roses,
A little straw hat to set off the blue ribbons,
    That tie up my bonnie brown hair.

Margaret W. Tarrant

Mary, Mary, Quite Contrary

"Mary, Mary, quite contrary,
    How does your garden grow?"
"With silver bells, and cockle shells
    And pretty maids all in a row."

Little Boy Blue

Little Boy Blue, come
　　Blow up your horn,
The sheep's in the meadow,
　　The cow's in the corn.

Where is the boy who
　　Looks after the sheep?
Under the haystack,
　　Fast asleep.

Ride a Cock-horse
to Banbury Cross

Ride a Cock-horse,
To Banbury Cross
To see a fine lady
Ride on a white horse.

Rings on her fingers
And bells on her toes,
She shall have music
Wherever she goes.

Rock-a-bye Baby

Rock-a-bye baby,
   On the tree top,
When the wind blows,
   The cradle will rock.

When the bough breaks,
   The cradle will fall,
Down will come baby,
   Cradle and all.

About Margaret Tarrant

Margaret Winifred Tarrant (1888–1959) was born in Battersea, England, the only child of the landscape artist, Percy Tarrant. She was encouraged to draw and paint from an early age and is best known for her charming illustrations of young children, fairies and animals. Working in various media, including pen and ink, watercolour and graphite, she began working for Christmas card publishers at the age of 18, before illustrating Charles Kingsley's *Water Babies* two years later. Tarrant attended several art schools, including Guildford School of Art, and exhibited at the Royal Academy and the Royal Society of Artists in Birmingham. Over the years she produced illustrations for many books, including an edition of *Alice's Adventures in Wonderland*, Harry Golding's *Verses for Children*, many books of nursery rhymes, and a popular series of fairy books written by Marion St John Webb. Her illustrations have also appeared on postcards, calendars, greeting cards and prints, and remain popular today.

This edition first published 2011 by The O'Brien Press Ltd.,
12 Terenure Road East, Rathgar, Dublin 6, Ireland
E-mail:books@obrien.ie
Website:www.obrien.ie

ISBN: 978-1-84717-235-8

Originally published 2009 by Mallon Publishing, Australia
Designer Lynn Twelftree
Editor Margaret Trudgeon

British Library Cataloguing-in-Publication Data
A catalogue record for this title is available from the British Library

1 2 3 4 5 6 7
11 12 13 14 15

Printed by Tien Wah Press Pte Ltd, Singapore